The King and I

Stories told by Jesus about God's kingdom

Jesus and You: The King and I
© Pete and Anne Woodcock/The Good Book Company 2012

Published by

The Good Book Company Ltd
1 Blenheim Road
Epsom, Surrey KT19 9AP, UK
Tel (UK): 0333 123 0880
Tel (Int): (+44) 208 942 0880
email: admin@thegoodbook.co.uk

Websites

UK: www.thegoodbook.co.uk
North America: www.thegoodbook.com
Australia: www.thegoodbook.com.au
New Zealand: www.thegoodbook.co.nz

ISBN: 9781905564354
Printed in China
Design by André Parker

Contents

This handbook is designed to be used with the **Jesus and You: The King and I DVD** also available from The Good Book Company. (DVD ISBN: 9781905564606)

A free downloadable **Leader's Guide** is available on our website: **www.thegoodbook.co.uk/thekingandi**

Welcome to The King and I

We hope that you will enjoy these four sessions. They will introduce you to Jesus Christ and his teaching.

In this booklet you will find a number of things to help you:

- Questions that you can talk about in your group

- Space to write down what you learn, if you want to

- The parts of the Bible that we will look at

- A summary of each DVD talk that we will watch

- Space to write down your own questions, comments or problems

The King and I is for anyone and everyone who wants to find out about Jesus Christ. This means that...

- some of you know something about these stories of Jesus—but some of you don't know anything.

- some of you have been to church—but some of you are completely new to the Christian faith.

- some of you enjoy reading, writing and studying—but some of you haven't done this for years, and perhaps you never enjoyed it even then.

- some of you may be learning to speak English.

Whoever you are, don't worry—your group leader will help you and will explain everything you need to know.

So, time to get started and get into **The King and I**...

1 The four soils
Matthew 13 v 1-23

Think about messages...

■ What messages have you received today? Where or how?

■ Which ones do you follow most?

The story

■ Listen to the story Jesus told: Matthew 13 v 1-23.
■ You can read it for yourself on p22.

You can read it for yourself on p22.

Optional extra

Test yourself: How much can you remember?
Answer the questions (in pairs, if you prefer).

A   Jesus was teaching...

   a in a house.
   b on the shore of a lake.
   c in a boat.

B   Jesus told a story about...

   a a good farmer.
   b a bad farmer.
   c a farmer (it doesn't matter if he was good or bad).

C   In Jesus' story...

   a most of the seed didn't grow.
   b most of the seed grew, but didn't produce a crop.
   c most of the seed produced a crop.

D   **a** Everyone understood the meaning of Jesus' story.
   b The disciples learned the meaning of Jesus' story from Jesus.
   c Jesus' story doesn't have any special meaning.

E   Jesus said that people don't understand his teaching because...

   a they have hearing problems.
   b they are stubborn—they don't want to listen and understand.
   c his teaching is very difficult to understand.

F   Jesus' followers are like...

   a all four kinds of soil.
   b the rocky, the weedy and the good soils, where the seed grows.
   c the good soil, where the seed produces a crop.

Only half the story

Listen to the first part of the story again: Matthew 13 v 1-17
You can read it for yourself on p22-23.

Think about it

1.   Who heard what?

■   The crowd (v 2-3)

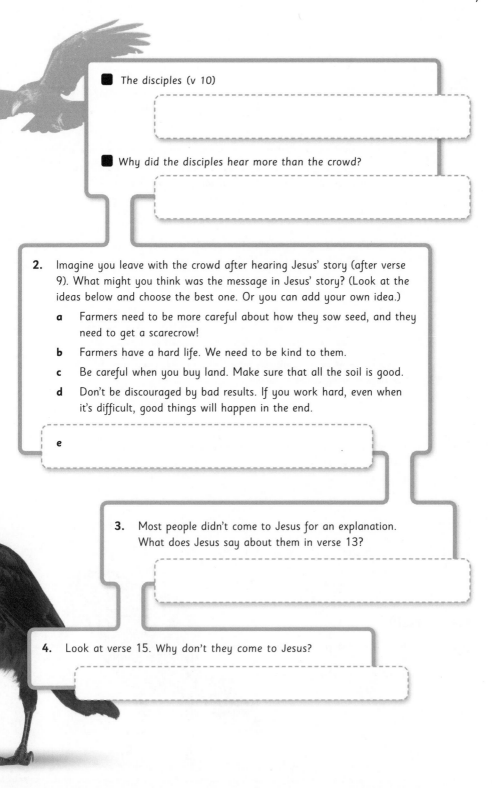

■ The disciples (v 10)

■ Why did the disciples hear more than the crowd?

2. Imagine you leave with the crowd after hearing Jesus' story (after verse 9). What might you think was the message in Jesus' story? (Look at the ideas below and choose the best one. Or you can add your own idea.)

a Farmers need to be more careful about how they sow seed, and they need to get a scarecrow!

b Farmers have a hard life. We need to be kind to them.

c Be careful when you buy land. Make sure that all the soil is good.

d Don't be discouraged by bad results. If you work hard, even when it's difficult, good things will happen in the end.

e

3. Most people didn't come to Jesus for an explanation. What does Jesus say about them in verse 13?

4. Look at verse 15. Why don't they come to Jesus?

DOWNLOAD 1:1

(Summary on p44)

5. Look at verse 15. People don't listen to Jesus because they are stubborn. What does it mean to be stubborn?

Why do you think they are stubborn?

6. In verse 16 Jesus says his disciples are "blessed". What does it mean to be blessed?

Why are they blessed?

Ask yourself:

Who am I most like—the crowd or the disciples?

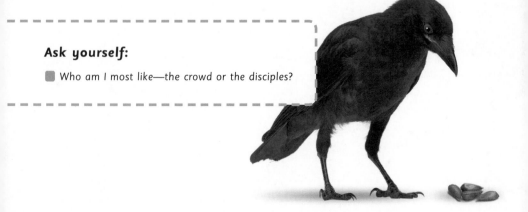

Four kinds of soil

Listen to the next part of the story: Matthew 13 v 18-23
You can read it for yourself on p23.

Think about it

1. The different types of soil are pictures of different types of people.
    Look at the first three types of soil (v 4-7) and people (v 19-22).

A. The path (verse 4)	The people (verse 19)
What happens to the seed at first?	What happens to the message at first?
What stops the seed growing?	What stops these people understanding?

B. The rocky soil (verses 5-6)	The people (verses 20-21)
What happens to the seed at first?	What happens to the message at first?
What stops the seed growing?	What stops these people producing a crop?

C. The weedy soil (verse 7)	The people (verse 22)
What happens to the seed at first?	What happens to the message at first?
What stops the seed growing?	What stops these people producing a crop?

2. Look at the fourth type of soil/person in verses 8 and 23. Why does the fourth type of person "produce a crop" when they hear the message about the kingdom?

■ What does "producing a crop" mean, do you think?

3. What do we need to do to understand Jesus' message about the kingdom?

DOWNLOAD 1:2

(Summary on p44)

4. In what ways have you seen people living like one of the first three soils?

Ask yourself:

■ Up till now, which soil best describes me?

Good soil

Think about it

1. Jesus says people are blind and stubborn. So what hope is there for us?

DOWNLOAD 1:3

(Summary on p44)

The big question

▪ Where are you in this story?

In another part of the Bible Jesus says:

"I tell you the truth, whoever hears my word and believes him who sent me has eternal life and will not be condemned; he has crossed over from death to life."

John 5 v 24 (The Bible: 1984 New International Version)

My questions and comments

2 The weeds and the wheat
Matthew 13 v 24-30 and 36-43

Summary so far:

Jesus is the king sent by God. Life in God's kingdom begins with him. We need to listen to Jesus.

Think about our world...

What things make people ask this question:
"Why doesn't God do something about the bad stuff in this world?"

The question we are going to think about is this:
Jesus says he is the king sent by God, bringing God's kingdom. So why isn't the world full of peace and goodness?

"The son of Man"
This is a title Jesus often used for himself.

The story

Listen to the story that Jesus told:
Matthew 13 v 24-30 and 36-43
You can read it for yourself on p24-25.

Optional extra

Test yourself: How much can you remember?
Answer the true or false questions (in pairs, if you prefer).

a The story of the weeds and wheat is about the kingdom of heaven. **T / F**

b The problem is that the farmer is rubbish at his job. **T / F**

c The problem is that the farmer's seed is full of weed seeds. **T / F**

d The problem is that the farmer's enemy wants to spoil his work. **T / F**

e If the farmer pulls up the weeds now, he will destroy the wheat. **T / F**

f If the farmer waits till harvest time, he will be able to harvest the wheat and destroy the weeds. **T / F**

g Jesus told the meaning of the story to everyone who heard the story. **T / F**

h The harvest is a picture of judgment day. **T / F**

i On judgment day first everyone will be punished, and then everyone will be let into God's kingdom. **T / F**

A mixed-up world

Listen again to the story and the first part of Jesus' explanation: Matthew 13 v 24-30 and 36-39

You can read it for yourself on p24.

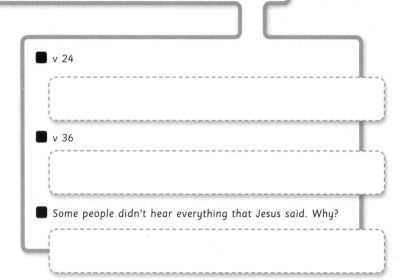

Think about it

1. Look at verses 24 and 36. Who heard what?

■ v 24

■ v 36

■ Some people didn't hear everything that Jesus said. Why?

2. What does each thing in the story mean? (Look at the verses to find each answer.)

Story	Meaning	
The man who sows good seed	Verse 37	
The field	Verse 38	
The good seed	Verse 38	
The enemy	Verse 39	
The weeds	Verse 38	
The harvest	Verse 39	
The servants/workers	Verse 39	

3. In Jesus' story there are weeds among wheat. This world isn't a place of peace and goodness because of those weeds.

Why is this world full of weeds? Find two answers in Jesus' story.

v 25

v 29

DOWNLOAD 2:1

(Summary on p45)

4. According to Jesus, what kind of person is "wheat"? And what kind of person is a "weed"?

■ Think of ways in which "weeds" might think they are "wheat".

5. Jesus teaches that there is an enemy—the devil—at work in this world. Have you ever heard of or thought about this before?

■ What difference should this make to you?

Ask yourself:

■ Am I a "weed" or "wheat"?

A merciful delay

Think about it

1. Look at verse 28. What do the servants want to do?

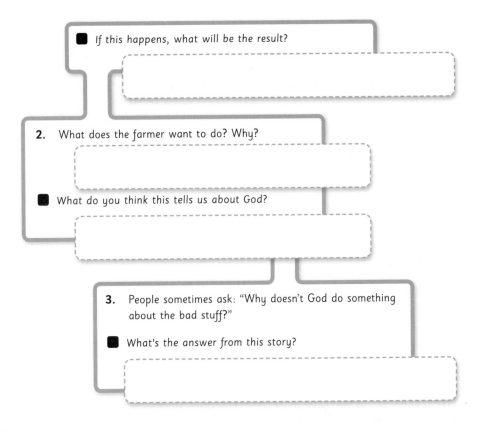

■ If this happens, what will be the result?

2. What does the farmer want to do? Why?

■ What do you think this tells us about God?

3. People sometimes ask: "Why doesn't God do something about the bad stuff?"

■ What's the answer from this story?

 DOWNLOAD 2:2

(Summary on p45)

There is something that this story doesn't mention: "weeds" can become "wheat".

Look at this verse from another part of the Bible:

"The Lord … is patient with you. He doesn't want anyone to be destroyed. Instead, he wants all people to turn away from their sins."

2 Peter 3 v 9

4. People give different reasons for why Jesus doesn't judge evil now.

- He doesn't really care about evil.
- He doesn't judge us because he's on our side—so we must be ok.
- God is all about love and forgiveness. It's wrong to think of him as our judge.
- We're not that bad. We don't need to be judged by Jesus.

■ But why isn't evil judged now, according to Jesus?

Ask yourself:

- How am I using this time of God's patience, when he is not judging evil?

The moment of division

Listen again to the last part of Jesus' explanation of his story: Matthew 13 v 30 and 39-43
You can read it for yourself on p24-25.

Think about it

1. From these verses, what is everyone heading towards?

2. What does the farmer do with the wheat?

■ What does he do with the weeds?

3. What will Jesus do?

4. Why will he do this, do you think?

DOWNLOAD 2:3

(Summary on p46)

The big question

■ Where are you in this story?

"Don't you know that evil people will not receive God's kingdom? Don't be fooled. Those who commit sexual sins will not receive the kingdom. Neither will those who worship statues of gods or commit adultery. Neither will men who are prostitutes or who commit homosexual acts. Neither will thieves or those who always want more and more. Neither will those who are often drunk or tell lies or cheat. People who live like that will not receive God's kingdom.

"Some of you used to do those things. But your sins were washed away. You were made holy. You were made right with God. All of that was done in the name of the Lord Jesus Christ and by the Spirit of our God."

1 Corinthians 6 v 9-11 (The Bible: New International Reader's Version)

My questions and comments

Bible text pull-out section

You can pull this section (p21-28) out of your handbook.
It contains the Bible text for all four sessions, and all other
Bible verses mentioned in the downloads.

1 Bible text

The four soils
Matthew 13 v 1-23

1   That same day Jesus left the house and sat by the Sea of Galilee.

2   Large crowds gathered around him. So he got into a boat. He sat down in it. All the people stood on the shore.

3   Then he told them many things by using stories. He said, "A farmer went out to plant his seed.

4   "He scattered the seed on the ground. Some fell on a path. Birds came and ate it up.

5   "Some seed fell on rocky places, where there wasn't much soil. The plants came up quickly, because the soil wasn't deep.

6   "When the sun came up, it burned the plants. They dried up because they had no roots.

7   "Other seed fell among thorns. The thorns grew up and crowded out the plants.

8   "Still other seed fell on good soil. It produced a crop 100, 60 or 30 times more than what was planted.

9   "Those who have ears should listen."

10   The disciples came to him. They asked, "Why do you use stories when you speak to the people?"

11   He replied, "You have been given the chance to understand the secrets of the kingdom of heaven. It has not been given to outsiders.

12   "Everyone who has that kind of knowledge will be given more. In fact, they will have very much. If anyone doesn't have that kind of knowledge, even what little he has will be taken away from him.

13 "Here is why I use stories when I speak to the people. I say, 'They look, but they don't really see. They listen, but they don't really hear or understand.'

14 "In them the words of the prophet Isaiah come true. He said,
'You will hear but never understand. You will see but never know what you are seeing.

15 " 'The hearts of these people have become stubborn. They can barely hear with their ears. They have closed their eyes. Otherwise they might see with their eyes. They might hear with their ears. They might understand with their hearts. They might turn to the Lord, and then he would heal them.' (Isaiah 6 v 9, 10)

16 "But blessed are your eyes because they see. And blessed are your ears because they hear.

17 "What I'm about to tell you is true. Many prophets and godly people wanted to see what you see. But they didn't see it. They wanted to hear what you hear. But they didn't hear it.

18 "Listen! Here is the meaning of the story of the farmer.

19 "People hear the message about the kingdom but do not understand it. Then the evil one comes. He steals what was planted in their hearts. Those people are like the seed planted on a path.

20 "Others received the seed that fell on rocky places. They are those who hear the message and at once receive it with joy.

21 "But they have no roots. So they last only a short time. They quickly fall away from the faith when trouble or suffering comes because of the message.

22 "Others received the seed that fell among the thorns. They are those who hear the message. But then the worries of this life and the false promises of wealth crowd it out. They keep it from producing fruit.

23 "But still others received the seed that fell on good soil. They are those who hear the message and understand it. They produce a crop 100, 60 or 30 times more than the farmer planted."

DOWNLOAD 1:2

Jeremiah 2 v 13

"My people have sinned twice. They have left me, even though I am the spring of water that gives life. And they have dug their own wells. But those wells are broken. They can't hold any water."

2 Bible text

The weeds and the wheat
Matthew 13 v 24-30 and 36-43

24 Jesus told the crowd another story. "Here is what the kingdom of heaven is like," he said. "A man planted good seed in his field.

25 "But while everyone was sleeping, his enemy came. The enemy planted weeds among the wheat and then went away.

26 "The wheat began to grow and form grain. At the same time, weeds appeared.

27 "The owner's servants came to him. They said, 'Sir, didn't you plant good seed in your field? Then where did the weeds come from?'

28 " 'An enemy did this,' he replied. The servants asked him, 'Do you want us to go and pull the weeds up?'

29 " 'No,' the owner answered. 'While you are pulling up the weeds, you might pull up the wheat with them.

30 " 'Let both grow together until the harvest. At that time I will tell the workers what to do. Here is what I will say to them. First collect the weeds. Tie them in bundles to be burned. Then gather the wheat. Bring it into my storeroom.' "

- -

36 Then Jesus left the crowd and went into the house. His disciples came to him. They said, "Explain to us the story of the weeds in the field."

37 He answered, "The one who planted the good seed is the Son of Man.

38 "The field is the world. The good seed stands for the people who belong to the kingdom. The weeds are the people who belong to the evil one.

39 "The enemy who plants them is the devil. The harvest is judgment day. And the workers are angels."

40 "The weeds are pulled up and burned in the fire. That is how it will be on judgment day.

41 "The Son of Man will send out his angels. They will weed out of his kingdom everything that causes sin. They will also get rid of all who do evil.

42 "They will throw them into the blazing furnace. There people will sob and grind their teeth.

43 "Then God's people will shine like the sun in their Father's kingdom. Those who have ears should listen."

DOWNLOAD 2:2

2 Peter 3 v 9

"The Lord ... is patient with you. He doesn't want anyone to be destroyed. Instead, he wants all people to turn away from their sins."

DOWNLOAD 2:2

Romans 2 v 4-5

"Do you make fun of God's great kindness and favour? Do you make fun of God when he is patient with you? Don't you realise that God's kindness is meant to turn you away from your sins? But you are stubborn. In your heart you are not sorry for your sins. You are storing up anger against yourself. The day of God's anger is coming. Then his way of judging fairly will be shown."

DOWNLOAD 2:3

Daniel 7 v 14

"He was given authority, glory and a kingdom. People from every nation and language worshipped him. His authority will last for ever. It will not pass away. His kingdom will never be destroyed."

3 Bible text

Seeds, yeast, treasure and a pearl Matthew 13 v 31-35 and 44-46

31 Jesus told the crowd another story. He said, "The kingdom of heaven is like a mustard seed. Someone took the seed and planted it in a field.

32 "It is the smallest of all your seeds. But when it grows, it is the largest of all garden plants. It becomes a tree. Birds come and rest in its branches."

33 Jesus told them still another story. "The kingdom of heaven is like yeast," he said. "A woman mixed it into a large amount of flour. The yeast worked its way all through the dough."

34 Jesus spoke all these things to the crowd by using stories. He did not say anything to them without telling a story.

35 So the words spoken by the prophet came true. He had said, "I will open my mouth and tell stories. I will speak about things that were hidden since the world was made." (from Psalm 78 v 2)

- -

44 "The kingdom of heaven is like treasure that was hidden in a field. When a man found it, he hid it again. He was very happy. So he went and sold everything he had. And he bought that field.

45 "Again, the kingdom of heaven is like a trader who was looking for fine pearls.

46 "He found one that was very valuable. So he went away and sold everything he had. And he bought that pearl."

DOWNLOAD 3:2
Revelation 1 v 8
(1984 NIV)

"I am [the one] who is and who was and who is to come, the Almighty."

 DOWNLOAD 3:2
Hebrews 1 v 3

"The Son is the gleaming brightness of God's glory. He is the exact likeness of God's being. He uses his powerful word to hold all things together. He provided the way for people to be made pure from sin."

 DOWNLOAD 3:2
Ephesians 1 v 7

"We have been set free because of what Christ has done. Through his blood our sins have been forgiven. We have been set free because God's grace is so rich."

4 Bible text

The net
Matthew 13 v 47-52

47 "Again, the kingdom of heaven is like a net. It was let down into the lake. It caught all kinds of fish.

48 "When it was full, the fishermen pulled it up on the shore. Then they sat down and gathered the good fish into baskets. But they threw the bad fish away.

49 "This is how it will be on judgment day. The angels will come. They will separate the people who did what is wrong from those who did what is right.

50 "They will throw the evil people into the blazing furnace. There the evil ones will sob and grind their teeth.

51 "Do you understand all these things?" Jesus asked. "Yes," they replied.

52 He said to them, "Every teacher of the law who has been taught about the kingdom of heaven is like the owner of a house. He brings new treasures out of his storeroom as well as old ones."

DOWNLOAD 4:1

Mark 7 v 20-23

"What comes out of people makes them 'unclean.' Evil thoughts come from the inside, from people's hearts. So do sexual sins, stealing and murder. Adultery, greed, hate and cheating come from people's hearts too. So do desires that are not pure, and wanting what belongs to others. And so do telling lies about others and being proud and being foolish. All those evil things come from inside a person. They make him 'unclean.' "

DOWNLOAD 4:1

Matthew 22 v 37-38

" 'Love the Lord your God with all your heart and with all your soul. Love him with all your mind.' This is the first and most important commandment."

3 Seeds, yeast, treasure and a pearl
Matthew 13 v 31-35 and 44-46

Summary so far:

▪ Jesus is the king sent by God. Life in God's kingdom begins with him. We need to listen to Jesus.

▪ If Jesus is the king sent by God, why is there evil in this world? Because Jesus is giving everyone the chance to be changed from weeds into wheat. Jesus the king will one day destroy all who belong to the evil one. We need to be changed by Jesus.

Think about nations that are super-powers...

▪ How do we know that a nation has become a super-power? How does it show that?

The story

▪ Listen to four very short stories that Jesus told: Matthew 13 v 31-35 and 44-46

▪ You can read them for yourself on p26.

30

Optional extra

Test yourself: How much can you remember?
Answer the questions (in pairs, if you prefer).

In the first story (v 31-32)...

  a What kind of seed is the kingdom of heaven like?
  b What does Jesus say about the seed?
  c What kind of plant does it grow into?

In the second story (v 33)...

  d What does yeast do when it is mixed with flour?

In the third story (v 44)...

  e What was the problem for the man who found the treasure?
  f What did he give up?
  g How did he feel about that?

In the fourth story (v 45-46)...

  h How is the story about the pearl like the story of the treasure?

The mustard seed and the yeast

Listen to the first two stories again: Matthew 13 v 31-35
You can read this for yourself on p26.

Think about it

1. Jesus uses the picture of a mustard seed. What does he want people to understand about the kingdom of heaven, do you think?

2. Jesus then uses the picture of yeast in a lump of dough. What does he want people to understand about the kingdom of heaven, do you think?

3. What's similar in these two stories? (Think about what happened to the seed and what would happen to the dough.)

DOWNLOAD 3:1

(Summary on p46)

4. Some people think of Jesus' death as just the sad end of a good man. Why is that wrong?

5. Many people think the message of Jesus is out-of-date, dull and useless. They think other messages sound better (how to make lots of money, how to be happy). Why is that wrong?

Ask yourself:

▪ Where am I in the story of the yeast?

   a I want nothing to do with the message of Jesus (like dough without any yeast).

   b Jesus is an add-on (I only think about him when I come to this group or when I go to church).

   c The message of Jesus is making me think about every part of my life (like dough with yeast in it).

The treasure and the pearl

Listen to the third and fourth stories again: Matthew 13 v 44-46
You can read this for yourself on p26.

Think about it

1. What do people think when they hear the name "Jesus"?

2. Jesus uses the pictures of treasure in a field and a very valuable pearl.

■ What does he want us to understand about the kingdom of heaven?

3. Both men in Jesus' stories sell everything to buy the field and the pearl.

■ What does Jesus want us to understand from this?

DOWNLOAD 3:2

(Summary on p46-47)

4. Look back at your answers to question 1 above.
Why do people miss the answer that is in these two stories?

5. Why is Jesus worth living for more than...

■ money?

■ your family?

■ religion?

The men in the story didn't just gaze in wonder at the beauty of the treasure, like someone looking at the Crown Jewels. They made sure they owned it, and they were happy to own it.

Ask yourself:

■ Most people just pick up bits and pieces about Jesus from other people. How much time and thought and questioning (digging) have I given to finding out the truth about Jesus?

Digging for treasure

 **DOWNLOAD 3:3**

(Summary on p47)

The big question: Where are you in this story?

- I'm walking through the field over the treasure (I'm not even trying to understand who Jesus is).
- I'm admiring the treasure like people admire the Crown Jewels (I think Jesus is great but he's nothing much to do with my life).
- I'm going home to sell everything (I am beginning to discover how great Jesus is).

"The message of the cross seems foolish to those who are lost and dying. But it is God's power to us who are being saved."

1 Corinthians 1 v 18 (The Bible: New International Reader's Version)

"I consider everything to be nothing compared to knowing Christ Jesus my Lord. To know him is the best thing of all. Because of him I have lost everything. But I consider all of it to be garbage so I can get to know Christ."

Philippians 3 v 8 (The Bible: New International Reader's Version)

My questions and comments

4 The net
Matthew 13 v 47-52

Summary so far:

- Jesus is the king sent by God. Life in God's kingdom begins with him. We need to listen to Jesus.
- If Jesus is the king sent by God, why is there evil in this world? Because Jesus is giving everyone the chance to be changed from weeds into wheat. Jesus the king will destroy all who belong to the evil one. We need to be changed by Jesus.
- Jesus' kingdom seems small and unimportant. But no one can stop it growing. Jesus' rule changes every part of our lives. And nothing is more valuable than King Jesus. We need to live for Jesus.

Think about exams...

Or medicals, or job interviews, or driving tests.

- Why don't we like them?

- What do they show us about ourselves?

The story

- Listen to this short story that Jesus told: Matthew 13 v 47-52
- You can read it for yourself on p28.

Test yourself: How much can you remember?
Answer the questions (in pairs, if you prefer).

Jesus said: "Again, the kingdom of heaven is like a [1]_____.
It was let down into the lake. It caught all kinds of fish. When it was full, the
fishermen pulled it up on the shore. Then they sat down and gathered the good
fish into [2]_____. But they threw the bad fish away. This is how
it will be on [3]_____. The [4]_____ will come.
They will [5]_____ the people who did what is wrong from those
who did what is right. They will throw the [6]_____ into the
blazing [7]_____. There the evil ones will [8]_____
and grind their teeth." "Do you [9]_____ all these things?"
Jesus asked. "[10]_____," they replied. He said to them, "Every
teacher of the law who has been taught about the kingdom of heaven is like the
[11]_____. He brings new [12]_____ out of his
storeroom as well as old ones."

Separation

Listen to the story again: Matthew 13 v 47-50
You can read it for yourself on p28.

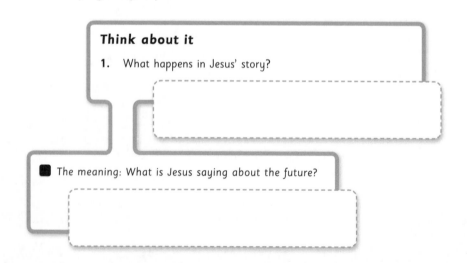

Think about it

1. What happens in Jesus' story?

The meaning: What is Jesus saying about the future?

2. Why are the fish separated into two groups?

■ The meaning: Why will people be separated into two groups?

3. Who will separate people into those two groups?

4. Most people prefer to sort people into groups like this:

   a Totally evil people (like Hitler or a child-murderer)
   b Very good people (like Nelson Mandela or a saint)
   c Good people who have done some bad things
   d Bad people who have done some good things

■ Which group would you put yourself in?

■ How would Jesus separate these people into two groups, do you think?

5. We can easily understand that there are two kinds of fish—good fish and bad fish.

But why is it difficult to accept that there are only two groups of people—good and evil?

 DOWNLOAD 4:1

(Summary on p47)

6. Read this verse from the Bible book of Isaiah (Isaiah is speaking to God):

"All of us have become like someone who is 'unclean'. All of the good things we do are like polluted rags to you."

■ How is God's view of good and evil different from our view?

7. Think about what you have learned. This could be very new to you. How do you feel about Jesus' teaching here?

Ask yourself:

■ Whose flag am I under?

New treasures

Listen to what Jesus says at the end of all his stories: Matthew 13 v 51-52
You can read it for yourself on p28.

Think about it

1. Jesus has told seven stories about his kingdom.
   What is the big thing that Jesus now wants to see in his disciples?

2. What do you think Jesus means by "understand"?

■ How would you know that someone understands Jesus' teaching?

■ If they don't fully understand, what do they need to do?

 DOWNLOAD 4:2

(Summary on p47-48)

3. Is there any reason why Jesus can't change your heart?

Ask yourself:

■ Do I want Jesus to change my heart?

Who will be your king?

DOWNLOAD 4:3

(Summary on p48)

The big question

■ Who is my king?

"[Jesus] appeared as a man. He came down to the lowest level. He obeyed God completely, even though it led to his death. In fact, he died on a cross.

"So God lifted him up to the highest place. He gave him the name that is above every name.

"When the name of Jesus is spoken, everyone's knee will bow to worship him. Every knee in heaven and on earth and under the earth will bow to worship him. Everyone's mouth will say that Jesus Christ is Lord. And God the Father will receive the glory."

Philippians 2 v 8-11 (The Bible: New International Reader's Version)

My questions and comments

Downloads

Here is a summary of each Download to help you remember what was said.

DOWNLOAD 1:1

- Jesus says that this story of the farmer and the seeds has a meaning. It's about "the message about the kingdom".

- "The message about the kingdom" is God's message to us. It's all about Jesus—who he is, why he has come and what he has done.

- All other messages in our world can only help us in this life. They can't do what God's message can do; they can't give us life for ever.

- Only the disciples heard Jesus' explanation of his story, and so only they heard God's message. They were not cleverer than the crowd. It was because they came to Jesus and listened to him.

- You can't separate "the message about the kingdom" from Jesus. It's like trying to join the kingdom, but rejecting the king.

- If you don't come to Jesus to find out about God's kingdom, you are an "outsider"—the message of the kingdom is like a secret. But when you come to Jesus, he will help you understand God's message.

DOWNLOAD 1:2

- The four different types of soil show four ways to respond to Jesus' message about the kingdom. Right now every person is responding to the message in one of these ways.

- **The path** is a picture of people who don't want to listen to God's message. Their hearts are hard. The message goes in one ear and out of the other.

- **The rocky soil** is a picture of people who follow Jesus while everything is going well. But as soon as being a Christian causes problems, they give up.

- **The weedy soil** is a picture of people who want Jesus but they want other things too. The worries of this life and the false promises of wealth take over and squeeze out King Jesus.

- We respond to God's message in these ways because we are blind to who Jesus is. We think the messages of this world are better and that life with God would be dull and miserable.

- Jesus is the word of God. Life in the kingdom of God begins with him. To ignore him is complete madness.

DOWNLOAD 1:3

- The good soil is a picture of people who both hear the message about the kingdom, and understand it.
- They understand that Jesus is their king and nothing stops them following him—not the evil one, nor suffering and troubles, nor the worries of this life, nor the false promises of wealth.
- You can see that they have understood the message by the difference that it makes in their lives.
- No one is born like the good soil. People become like the good soil when they come to Jesus, just as the disciples did.
- What will you do with God's message about the kingdom?

DOWNLOAD 2:1

- If Jesus is the king sent by God, bringing God's kingdom, why isn't the world full of peace and goodness? Because people refuse to have Jesus as their king.
- The **wheat** seed represents people who belong to the kingdom of heaven. The **weed** seed represents people who don't belong to God's kingdom. Instead, they belong to the evil one, God's enemy.
- People who belong to the evil one may look like people who belong to the kingdom of heaven. But over time the difference becomes clearer. On judgment day the difference will be clear for all to see.
- In this world good and evil grow side by side and everyone belongs to one of these two groups.
- The thing that divides everyone into these two groups is this: do you or don't you accept Jesus as your king?
- Many people think that they are living good lives but actually they are rebels against King Jesus.

DOWNLOAD 2:2

- People often want all evil taken out of the world now, but Jesus is waiting patiently for judgment day.
- Just because Jesus is patient, we mustn't think that he isn't bothered about evil, or that he will never judge us.
- Jesus is patient because he wants us to hear the message of the kingdom and change.
- If Jesus judges evil now, he will have to judge us now. That means we will be destroyed like the weeds, not saved like the wheat.
- By the kindness and mercy of God, people who are "weeds" today can become "wheat". They can be changed by Jesus.
- This time of Jesus' patience is time for you to turn to Jesus and accept him as your king. Make sure you belong to the kingdom of heaven before judgment day.

DOWNLOAD 2:3

- Our lives are heading towards judgment day. So what we do with Jesus now has consequences that last for ever.
- Jesus is the "Son of Man". That means that Jesus is the king of an everlasting kingdom given to him by God. And in Jesus' kingdom there are people from every nation and language.
- These people have all been changed by Jesus—cleansed by Jesus' death on the cross, and made into children of God.
- Only righteous people can belong to Jesus' kingdom. Righteous people have been made right with God, through Jesus' death on the cross.
- Jesus, the king of God's everlasting kingdom, is the one who decides who will come into the kingdom (the wheat) and who will not (the weeds).
- What happens on judgment day will reflect our response to King Jesus now. Those who accept Jesus as king will live in the light, life and warmth of his kingdom for ever. Those who reject Jesus as king will suffer ruin outside his kingdom for ever.

DOWNLOAD 3:1

- The stories of the mustard seed and the yeast teach us that the kingdom of heaven is very different to kingdoms in this world.
- Like a mustard seed, the kingdom of heaven looks like nothing, and the king of heaven, Jesus, doesn't look impressive.
- But the message of the kingdom, when understood and planted into someone's life, has a massive effect in their life.
- The message of the kingdom is that Jesus died so we can be forgiven, cleansed and made new.
- The story of the yeast teaches us that the kingdom of heaven grows in a way that is unnoticed in this world.
- The story of the yeast also teaches us that the message of Jesus will change every part of your life, just as the yeast affects every part of the dough.

DOWNLOAD 3:2

- In the stories of the treasure and the pearl, the two men look as if they are giving up everything. But in fact they are only giving up rubbish to gain everything.
- These two stories are a picture of the person who finds the kingdom of heaven because they come to understand who Jesus really is.
- Jesus is the only one who can bring us into the fantastic riches of the kingdom of heaven. So Jesus is the treasure and the pearl.
- Like the treasure in the field, the kingdom of heaven is hidden from us so we have to dig to find it. When you start to dig into the Bible, you find heaps of amazing things about Jesus.

- Everything you have or do in this world will end or die, but Jesus won't. Nothing you say or do or achieve can buy you a place in the kingdom of heaven, but Jesus can.
- These stories are not about giving up things to buy our way into God's kingdom. They are about understanding just how rich the treasure of Jesus is.

DOWNLOAD 3:3

- These four little stories of Jesus are themselves like mustard seeds—when they are planted in our hearts, they produce life that changes everything in our lives.
- Perhaps you are interested in Jesus but you just can't see that he is the greatest treasure. Then be like the disciples, and not the crowd. Come to Jesus and ask him to help you understand.

DOWNLOAD 4:1

- Jesus' story of the net is about judgment day, when Jesus will return as king of the universe to bring this world to a close.
- At that time, God's people had lots of religious rules about food. The good or "clean" fish are those that could be eaten. The bad or "unclean" fish are those that must not be eaten.
- Jesus says all people will be separated, like the fish, into those who are clean (who have done what's right) and those who are unclean (who have done what's wrong).
- Jesus says that the wrong things we do show that there is something wrong with our hearts. This puts all of us in the "bad fish" category.
- If Jesus is not your king, you are under the wrong flag, and everything you do is wrong—even the right things!
- Jesus lovingly warns us that if we say "No" to Jesus as our king, we will be separated from God's love for ever.

DOWNLOAD 4:2

- Although the story doesn't say this, Jesus has come to make unclean people clean before God and good in his eyes. The king has come to bring you into his kingdom.
- For this to happen we need a radical heart-change and only Jesus can do that.
- Jesus is saying that if you have understood his message, then it will make a change in your life.

- Instead of bad things, treasures will come out of our hearts—the treasure of Jesus. Changed hearts are hearts that love, follow and live for King Jesus.
- Jesus says that even the worst people, like the teachers of the law who hated him and who were far away from God, can be changed by Jesus and join the kingdom of heaven.
- If someone like that can have a heart-change, then so can everyone.

DOWNLOAD 4:3

- Jesus wants us to understand all the things he teaches. It's not enough just to hear them.
- These are not just nice little stories—they are matters of heaven and hell, your eternal destiny, and who your king is.
- We have learned a lot about who Jesus is—the greatest treasure, the seed of life, the gleaming brightness of God, the one who gave up his life for us, the only one who can pay the penalty for our sin, the one who can change us, the king.
- Is Jesus your king?